# Foreword

This book has evolved from a talk that I have given to many groups and societies. I have spoken at a venue near to the remarkable basalt columns of the Giant's Causeway on Northern Ireland's scenic northern coast and given talks in sight of the clean-cut chalk cliffs where the Downs meet the sea on the Sussex and Kent coast and at many places in between. Weather Lore–Fact or Fiction? always proves a popular subject.

These pages are intended as a practical guide for outdoor people in making their own weather forecast. In many ways being weather-wise is common sense and stems from good observation and recognition of the many clues around us. An almost infinite host of weather sayings have arisen about this subject. Just how reliable they are provides the basis of this book.

**Ian Currie   Autumn 2010**

radmore Green, Old Coulsdon April 1997 showing cirrus fibratus and floccus cloud.

**A dissipating shower at sunset on April 19th 2004 looking west from Bidborough in Kent.**

The weather comes up in most of our conversations as the writer Samuel Johnson penned in the eighteenth century, *"When two Englishmen meet, their first talk is of the weather"*.

Not surprising as it can be said that the British Isles lies at the crossroads of the world's weather and *'every wind has its weather'*. Certainly it is seldom out of the news and can quickly turn a lovely day out into a miserable rain-soaked and wind-lashed experience. If only we could tell what the weather is going to do. Well, you can and it does not involve super computers, expensive instruments or a degree in atmospheric physics. Often we only wish to know if it is going to rain for an hour or two ahead. Will that washing dry out in the garden during the morning or should we carry an umbrella when we walk to the local shops? For this in particular we can turn to weather lore. The translation of an old French adage tells us to *'wait until nightfall before saying it has been a fine day'* but perhaps we could use the signs around us to forecast this in advance.

**Altocumulus castellanus floccus cloud, a sure sign of impending thundery conditions on June 23rd 1994 in Coulsdon, Surrey. The next day brought thunderstorms.**

A fine afternoon in Marlow, Buckinghamshire, during February 1996.

However, there is much myth and legend attached to what is often regarded as the 'country way of forecasting'. Some sayings have less sense than others though many are often quite humorous. *'When a fly lands on your nose, swat it 'til it goes. When it lands back again, watch out for some heavy rain'.* Or *'If the hairs on a cat stand up, it means approaching rain–or a dog'*! Another tells us, *'Spring has arrived when a lady can stand on seven daisies at once'.*

Actually this latter one has some sense as it really alludes to soil temperatures with true spring being when the soil has warmed up sufficiently for widespread flowering and not just a few warm days early on in the season.

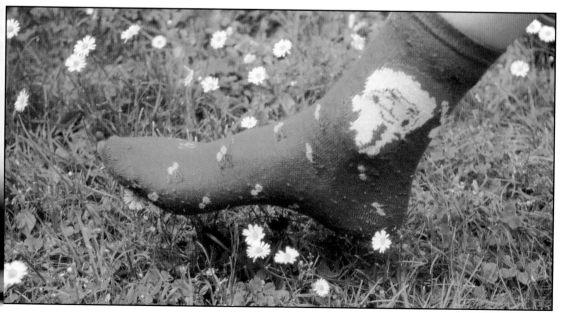

**Drawing by Sue Attwood**

Probably one of the most well-known from our rich vein of weather lore is the least accurate, '*Upon this day is St. Swithin's day on which it rain they say, for forty days after it wil or more or less some rain distil*'. Swithin was a ninth century monk who rose to become the Bishop of Winchester. He asked to be buried in "a vile and unworthy place, under the drips of eaves, so the sweet rain of heaven may fall on his grave". It was almost a hundred years later in AD 971 when he was reburied on the July 15th. Legend states the occasion was held up by tempestuous weather but this may well have been made up by Ben Jonson in the seventeenth century. Studies have shown that there is no truth in this saying and it simply does not 'hold water'.

**Berries on the bushes during the autumn of 2006, Chipstead Valley, Surrey.**

Other familiar but misleading weather notions include, *'Lots of berries on the bushes in early autumn means we are in for a severe winter'* and *'If it snows in New York, it will snow in London a week or so later'* or *'Thunderstorms go round in circles'* and *'Lightning cannot strike the same place twice'*. Often mentioned is *'Cows lying down are a sign of rain'* and *'If the oak comes before the ash we are in for a splash'* (meaning a dry summer) and the *'Ash before the oak, we are in for a soak'* (meaning a wet summer). The former occurred in many places in 2007 and the summer turned out to be the wettest in the national record.

There are still people who think that the moon's phases bring about changes to our weather but this old maxim sums up this notion perfectly, *'The moon and the weather may change together but a change in the moon does not alter the weather. If we had no moon at all and that may seem strange, we would still have weather that's subject to change'*.

Many weather sayings can be grouped into one of three main categories. Those that involve plants and animals; secondly saints days and special days, and lastly those that have arisen from folk who have lived and breathed under our skies in all weathers such as farmers, fishermen, sailors and shepherds.

Take a good look at the sky and if you have a barometer hanging on a wall where you live or work, inspect it. I will state a few reliable sayings about this useful instrument later on. The clues to the day's weather lie all around us and many are encapsulated in a delightful rhyme. Use those that are most suitable for your local area. You will then have a dependable forecast that works on more occasions than it fails.

So let's start with sayings about sky colour and the shape and type of cloud for they can be excellent indicators of future weather. For instance, a deep red at sunrise or yellow tints at sunset can be signs that rain is not far off and one of the most accurate sayings is *'a yellow sky to end the day, wind and rain are on the way'*.

**A yellow sky at sunset can be an ominous sign of increasingly unsettled conditions.**

Another, *"Red sky in the morning, shepherd's warning"* is mentioned in the Bible (Matthew 16 verse 2). The red in this case is due to the sun's rays shining onto high ice cloud called cirrus which are often the harbingers of an approaching bad weather system. A rainbow early in the morning can also be an unsettled sign. This shows the sun is shining out of the east onto rain falling from approaching shower clouds in the south-west, a typical direction in unsettled weather. Hence, *'Rainbow to windward, foul falls the day. Rainbow to leeward, damp runs away'*. The day can be particularly unsettled in this situation as normally showers tend to form later in the day when the land has warmed up. The early onset of showers denotes very unstable air.

**A rainbow seen during the late afternoon at Coulsdon, Surrey.**

**A fine sunset on the Dutch coast, the wisps of cirrus did not increase and the next day was fine.**

*"Red sky at night, shepherd's delight"* also mentioned in Matthew 16, is one of the oldest of weather adages. It has some validity if the reddish-orange coloration along the western horizon fades gradually to the zenith. The reds in this case are caused by dust particles picked up into the atmosphere by daytime heating in settled weather. They scatter light made up of the spectral colours but especially blue light. The more dust contained in the atmosphere the more scattering and diffusion takes place. Towards the evening, when the sun's light has an extended passage through the atmosphere due to its low angle, the longer wave lengths of orange and red predominate. The dust is trapped nearest to the ground by what is known as an inversion (a layer of air where the temperature actually rises with height instead of the normal cooling). This is quite common in areas of high pressure in which air is descending, drying and warming and results in spells of settled weather. If you can see the setting sun on the horizon and especially if you are looking from a hill top view point, there is unlikely to be any bad weather for hundreds of miles upstream. Most of our inclement weather comes in eastwards from off the Atlantic Ocean with cloud streaming out for great distances ahead of the rain, masking any sunset.

**Thickening high cloud denoting a change to more unsettled conditions coming in from the west over the damaged West Pier at Brighton giving this eye-catching sunset in January 2003. Picture by Robert Vanko.**

Check your barometer and if it is higher than, say, 1024 millibars (hPa) or 30.24 inches and continuing to rise, there is a good chance that the next day will be a 'window' of fine weather. Overnight, particularly if the wind is coming in off a cool sea surface such as the North Sea, the early morning may be cloudy but then it often brightens up, especially away from the east coast.

*'Evening red and morning grey, this is a sign of a bonnie day.*
*'Evening grey and morning red, the lamb and the ewe go wet to bed'.*
Or
*'Grey morning with a rising glass, fine weather will come to pass'.*

High pressure may not last all that long when it is in the form of a ridge or temporary area of increased pressure between two weather systems (in a fast moving weather situation) especially in the winter half of the year. At this time in particular we should perhaps take heed of Thomas Tusser, the well known 16th century poet and farmer, who wrote *"If the weather be fair, then tidy thy grain. Make speedy carriage for fear of rain. For tempest and showers deceiveth many and lingering lubbers lose many a penny"*. Another way of expressing this is, *'Make hay while the sun shines'*.

In unsettled weather visibility is often good (except in the rain or on the higher hills) due to impurities such as dust having been washed out of the atmosphere. Also the Atlantic, our chief source of rain, is an unpolluted direction. *'The farther the sight, the nearer the rain.'* Though if the wind backs to the south east we often get a haze from the continent. Even if the west coast tends to be wetter than further east perhaps it is too pessimistic to say, *'If you can see Lundy Isle it is going to rain, if you can't it is raining'*!

Turquoise or green coloration means increasing humidity or water content of the atmosphere so the weather does not auger well. Other signs of rain are a halo or circles that can be seen around the sun or moon, caused by the refraction or bending of sunlight as it passes through crystals of ice. Cirrus clouds that produce this phenomenon are around 5 to 6 miles high or more and can often be the advance guards of a bad weather system.

especially if they thicken to a milky white sheen called cirrostratus. It is easier to see this sign around the moon. The weather saying that goes with this effect runs, *'if there is a halo round the sun or moon, then we can all expect rain quite soon'*. This is particularly true if the air pressure is showing signs of a sustained fall. For, *'nasty nature the roll of lows, rainy days and windy blows'*. More about air pressure later.

**Cirrus uncinus or hooked shaped cirrus on the right and cirrostratus to the left as a frontal system approaches.**

Cirrus clouds can make some beautiful delicate shapes, *'Mare's tails, mare's tails, make tall ships carry low sails'* or *'If the sky describes the painter's brush, soon around you winds will rush'*.

**A halo around the sun, with red coloration on the outside showing that it is caused by refraction of light passing through ice crystals making up thin cirrus cloud. A single rainbow on the other hand has red on the outside (see page 5) and is caused by reflection of raindrops.**

Cloud may then continue to thicken, *'If the sun's shining pale with a watery eye, be sure a soaking ere nightfall is nigh'*; If the *'moon rises pale, expect rain'*. Cloud becomes more dense and a grey swathe of altostratus obscures the sun or moon. Then, with the first drops of rain or flakes of snow, it is the rain cloud nimbostratus that now fills the sky synonymous with a wet spell so *'lowering skies, lowering skies, stay indoors if you are wise'*. The rain typically lasts for about four to six hours and hence *'rain before seven, fine before eleven' does have an element of truth to it'*.

Most of our rain comes in from the Atlantic but occasionally it arrives from the east and can be both heavy and persistent. *'Rain from the east, lasts a day at least'*. Quite often though, if the wind is from the east or north-east it brings a dry spell. Springtime in particular is prone to winds from this direction. There is an old and quite accurate saying attributed to the Shepherd of Banbury (likely to be John Claridge) and printed in 1774 that says, *"If the wind is in the north-east for three days without rain, eight days will pass before the wind is south again"*. This is useful for growers following a wet winter when evaporation has been low and the soil is saturated. A period of dry weather in March is needed to get out and work the fields, garden or allotment and so *'a peck of March dust is worth a king's ransom in gold'*. Be careful, though, with an east wind as it can feel very chilly in the spring, especially so if you are beside the cold North Sea, *'when the wind is from the east 'tis neither good for man nor beast'*. Indeed, during winter this wind direction can bring us our coldest weather with sharp frosts and even snow showers especially in eastern coastal counties.

**Altostratus giving a watery or milky look to the sun. Rain or snow is not far away.**

**Nimbostratus or rain-cloud giving a wet day at Brighton on the Sussex coast.**

One of my favourite skies is a 'mackerel sky' that really does look like the scales of a fish. This cloud is called cirrocumulus and is often above 5 miles in height and is made up of minute ice crystals. Large scale lifting of an air mass on the edge of an approaching low-pressure system causes abrupt changes of wind direction and speed with height, known as 'shear' and can generate this cloud type. So quick-change weather can be expected hence *'mackerel sky, mackerel sky, never long wet and never long dry'*. This effect can also occur in altocumulus cloud though the elements are larger and less delicate.

**A 'mackerel sky' looking like the scales of a fish with unsettled conditions moving in from the west. Also a yellowish-white coloration is a changeable sign.**

When clouds tower up like mountains or cliffs this is an indication that the air mass is highly unstable with the air temperature decreasing rapidly with height. It also shows there is plenty of moisture available too. Parcels of rising air called thermals quickly form large convective cloud that is quite likely to lead to a sudden downpour or even a thunderstorm. Hence, *'If in the sky you see cliffs and towers it won't be long before there are showers'*.

**A wall of cumulonimbus cloud looking north-from near Isfield, East Sussex, generating thunderstorms in the north of Sussex and Surrey on the July 24th 2009.**

These clouds which can grow to over 8 miles in height are called cumulonimbus or thunder-clouds. A weather saying that could save your life tells us, *'Beware of the oak it courts the stroke, avoid the ash it attracts the flash'*. Oak and ash trees are often struck by lightning from these powerful clouds for a number of reasons. For example they have a high moisture content, often stand tall and solitary in a field plus they have a deep tap root. Another old axiom is *'thunderstorms come up against the wind'* which has some truth for a large convective storm can have an inflow of warm moist air whilst the bulk of the cloud system is moving with the upper wind at odds with the surface current.

A storm may also form on a frontal system at the boundary of an air mass, especially a cold front or an occlusion (the latter is when the warm air mass has been lifted entirely from the surface). Now and then thunderstorms may develop along a warm front. The surface wind tends to back (move anticlockwise) from west to southeast ahead of an advancing front with the storm appearing to come in at a tangent. The storm itself travels in the direction of the front steered by upper winds, commonly west to east.

After a spell of fine warm weather in summer the weather can become more humid and thundery and a clue to this is altocumulus castellanus cloud (see bottom picture on page 1). Thunderstorms formed four hours after this picture was taken. The old maxim accredited sometimes to Charles II has a ring of truth to it, *"The British summer–three fine days and a thunderstorm"*.

**Lightning strike on a Douglas fir in Redhill, Surrey, May 1993.**

**Lightning out at sea off Hastings, East Sussex, circa 1909.**

**Cumulus humilus or flattened cumulus at Dorking in Surrey. A fine afternoon in September 2006.**

When the sky is partly covered by small 'cotton wool' type clouds, it is mid-morning and they are not growing larger, then a fine day can be expected. Thus, *'If woolly fleeces bestrew the heavenly way, be sure no rain will come today'*. These are fair weather cumulus whose bases generally lie about 800 to 1000 metres above the ground. Although they are the product of convective thermals, their growth tends to be limited by drier, stable air aloft and a lid to cloud development called an inversion. This latter feature explained earlier is common within high pressure and also helps towards making a fine, reddish-orange sunset.

If you have access to an aneroid barometer, a device that measures day to day changes in atmospheric pressure, you will often notice the needle indicating a fall in air pressure when the weather changes for the worse. The old name for a barometer is the 'weather glass'. The word 'aneroid' literally means without liquid and this type of device, invented by Lucien Vidie in 1843 is used widely. It relies on the force of air pressure upon a shallow capsule of thin corrugated metal, with levers and springs magnifying the movement and shown by a pointer. Hence an excellent adage is *'when the wind backs and the glass falls, be on your guard for rain or squalls'*.

Less common these days is the mercury barometer and of late there is an increasing use of electronic instruments. The same principles apply to these instruments. For example falling air pressure can mean worsening weather whilst rising air pressure may bring improving conditions. If the air pressure is steady then the weather conditions prevailing at the time will often persist. In the writer's locality inside the southern section of the London orbital motorway, one can use a more modern and land-based weather saying, *'When you can hear the sound of the M25, cloud and rain will surely arrive'*. Ahead of rain, the wind can often back round the compass

**Drawing by Sue Attwood.**

15

**The M25 motorway looking east from Reigate Hill, junction 8. A retreating cumulonimbus cloud has recently given a shower. Picture by Steven Currie.**

anticlockwise over the course of a day from west to south before rain arrives and increase in strength too as the low-pressure with its associated weather fronts comes nearer. When it is westerly the drone of the traffic cannot be heard.

Haloes, mackerel skies and yellow skies mentioned earlier are often associated with falling pressure. If you notice a sudden rise of the pressure from a depressed reading of, say, 980 millibars, when a low-pressure system passes by, the wind can strengthen quickly thus *'first rise after low, foretells an even greater blow'*. As the low-pressure moves away

16

the wind will now veer clockwise around the compass as every sailor knows, changing for example from southerly through west to north-west. This can be accompanied by a spell of heavy, squally rain before it brightens up and the wind eases.

High-pressure at, say, around 1030 millibars or hPa on a very modern barometer (30.42 inches on older instruments) is often likely to lead to fine weather. *'If the glass is high and rising still, no rain today no weather ill'*. But be careful as fog can form and persist in winter. Frosty nights are to be expected in areas of high-pressure that are cloud-free, hence *'clear moon, frost soon'*. In the lengthening nights of autumn high-pressure may well lead to dewy dawns but the weather can remain settled for several days thus, *'dew upon the grass, fine weather will come to pass'*.

Actually, in both winter and summer (when high-pressure prevails) it becomes increasingly hazy with dust trapped beneath the inversion mentioned earlier and *'the greater the haze, the more settled the weather'* is often true.

It is not only the skies where you can find clues to the day ahead. Try looking at plants and animals. But be careful! There is no truth in the saying that *'cows lying down means it is going to rain'*. They have simply had a lot to eat and are relaxing whilst digesting the meal and enjoying the view!

**Fog can form on some clear nights as the surface temperature falls and the air is sufficiently moist as here at St Margaret's Church, Hooley, Surrey. It then often dissipates during the morning.**

However, there is a plant that is known as the poor man's weather-glass. It is called the scarlet pimpernel whose orange-red flowers react to decreasing light and increasing humidity, that is the amount of water vapour in the air. If they are closed on a summer afternoon then the humidity of the air is quite likely to be above 80 per cent under a cloud cover and that is a potential for rain, *'the pimpernel whose leaves are spread, and flowers of pinky red close against a rainy hour'*. What a pity the plant only flowers for a few months of the year. It is said that the dandelion closes its flower when the temperature goes below 10C or so. This is something that the reader can test for his or herself as well as observing the rhododendron. Its leaves start to droop and curl at 2C, hang downward at 0C and sag downward tightly curled at minus 6C!

**The scarlett pimpernel, Anagallis arvensis, is known as the poor-man's weather-glass as it reacts to changing levels of humidity and light.**

*'Bees staying near the hive means cloud and rain are sure to arrive'*. Bees and other insects such as ants, are quite weather sensitive; so are some animals. Bees tend to swarm in dry, warm weather and in May there is much pollen hence, *'A swarm of bees in May, is worth a load of hay'*. Dogs can hear approaching thunderstorms too distant for humans to notice and they often scuttle away and hide. Again there is some credence to the axiom *'If birds be silent, expect thunder'*. This latter adage is more likely to be caused by the birds reacting to lowering light levels as the massive bulk of a cumulonimbus cloud approaches. The venturing inland of sea birds because of stormy conditions along the coast is a popular belief. True, winds are often twice as strong in coastal areas compared to locations well inland but these days it might be the lure of a landfill site that tempts seagulls away from the sea for easy pickings.

**February 2008 was the sunniest February on record and it was mild too. It brought out these bees at Bookham, Surrey. Picture by Keith Walter.**

How rooks take flight has long been thought to predict weather conditions such *'As a sudden dip in flight meaning rain likely'*. In my experience *'Swallows high, staying dry'* and *'When sky larks fly high and sing long, expect fine weather'* are more accurate. Even these can be misleading for ahead of showers powerful convective uplift can quite literally scoop insects up to higher levels and make a tasty meal for birds soaring far above the ground. Spring is the most fickle time of the year weather-wise, especially for temperature. Our surrounding seas are at their coldest, ice and snow still cover the Arctic and the overall temperature of the atmosphere is cool. March has a dangerous reputation accurately characterised by these sayings, *'If in March you have sun and heat, it won't be long before there is snow and sleet'* or *'If the birds are singing on St. David's Day, they will be silent by Lady Day'*, the 1st and 25th March respectively. The old Scandinavian proverb, *'As the days grow longer, the cold grows stronger'* often has more than a ring of truth to it. The winter of 2007/8 was mild and snowless across many parts of the UK, nevertheless it was followed by a 'white' Easter in March.

I have found no truth in the well-known prognosis that *'If March comes in like a lion* (meaning stormy), *it goes out like a lamb'* or vice versa.

In fact April can be even more capricious than March with the sun now rising higher in the sky and the air near the surface warming rapidly. But, within a polar air mass there can still be very cold air aloft associated with a steep lapse rate or fall of temperature with height, leading to wild fluctuations of temperature at ground level. Snow can fall in April in showery weather with an air temperature around 8C. But the temperature will then start to plunge dramatically in the heavier showers, down to freezing on some occasions, before rising again as the sun returns and the shower moves away. Shakespeare was near the mark when he wrote, *"The uncertain glory of an April day"*. The maxim, *'April has the face of a monk but the claws of a cat'* is often very accurate. It has been said that *'April can have four seasons in one day'*. Gardeners should not put out their delicate plants during this month without protection for *'Don't change a thread 'til April's dead'*. A night temperature below minus 5C is not uncommon during this month even in the south and it could be several degrees lower still further north. One must remember that there have been some notable late April snowstorms with the years 1908, 1950 and 1981 producing striking examples.

Aylesbury, Buckinghamshire, in late April 1908.

A long spell of warm spring weather does not necessarily provide immunity from a late frost. A good example was in the spring of 1997. Following a very balmy February and March, on April 21st the thermometer plummeted to around minus 5C just as blossom bedecked our orchards. It proved calamitous for fruit farmers. In some prone valleys in southern England it even plunged to minus 8C. Dry, polar air and the wind dropping out as clouds dissipate can often lead to *'Clear moon, frost soon'* or *'When the stars are clear and bright, we shall have a frosty night'*. The wind in such cold polar airstreams can often die down after sunset and there is more than a grain of truth to *'an honest man and a north west wind generally go to sleep together'*.

The autumn can be as capricious for rainfall as the spring is for temperature and it is no coincidence that quite a few counties have had their wettest day during this season. It is a time when the sea around our shores is at its warmest but the Arctic is starting to cool and this can trigger active frontal systems or heavy showers. *'September can dry up the wells or break down the bridges'*. A number of bridges were swept away in mid-September 1968, there were dramatic floods on the September 5th 1958 and in both September and October 2000. Sometimes, as in 1959 September brings little rain and in earlier centuries following a parched summer (in days before mains water was available) the wells could literally run dry.

The writer has looked into one autumn saying that has a bearing on the following winter. It sounds a somewhat bizarre adage but *'If the ice on a pond in November can bear the weight of a duck, then the winter will have only sludge and muck'* has some truth to it. In essence it is telling us that a cold November is likely to be followed by a mild winter with just soft unfrozen ground and wet conditions. Taking the period of 1820 to the present I identified 17 very cold Novembers, only 5 were followed by cold winters. It proved most accurate for the first half of the 20th century. From the 1930s and into the 21st century there have been a dearth of cold Novembers. Since 1980 only 1985 and marginally 1993 were in this category. The latter was followed by a mild winter whilst 1985/86 started mild but there was a very chilly February. The severe weather of November 2010 took place only during the last few days.

**Drawing by Sue Attwood.**

Now armed with an array of 'weather lore' and hopefully a heightened sense of observation you should be able to avoid that sudden, soaking shower. Of course, you can never be a hundred per cent correct all of the time and there are occasions when *rain before seven* persists all day. Indeed, during June 1903 it continued non-stop in many parts of the normally dry southeast for over 60 hours. It was probably a similar incident that prompted the following lines, *'The Duke of Rutland urged the folk to pray for rain. The rain came down the following day. The pious marvelled, the sceptics murmured fluke, but the farmers late with hay said, "Damn the Duke"*! Dennis Howell, appointed Minister for Drought in the blazing summer of 1976 achieved a similar effect.

And of course, everyone has his or her own interpretation of what is 'good' weather. But we can safely say, *'Whether the weather be cold, or whether the weather be hot.*
*Whether the weather be dry or whether the weather be not.*
*We'll weather the weather whatever the weather,*
*Whether we like it or not'.*

------------------

# About the Author – Ian Currie

The ever-changing moods and patterns of our skies have always fascinated Ian, an interest fuelled by the spectacular thunderstorm of September 1958 and the prolonged, deep snows during the 1962/3 winter. It nearly buried his own first weather station, childhood memories that have never faded. Indeed Ian has such an enthusiasm for the whole topic of weather that he is now a full-time freelance weatherman, author and speaker and is editor of Weather eye magazine which he founded for people to share in his fascination for the subject.

Ian is a graduate of geography and earth science and was a teacher for 20 years. Having both successfully forecast and experienced first-hand the raging tempest of October 1987, this storm proved a major factor in blowing him in new directions and has subsequently become quite a prolific writer. He co-authored 'Surrey in the Hurricane' and a follow-up London version. He then became the weatherman and co-author behind a series of books about the weather in Surrey, Kent, Sussex, Essex, Hampshire and the Isle of Wight, plus Norfolk, Suffolk, Berkshire and Dorset. Each of these books includes a pictorial record of storms, floods and freezes, droughts and dust-devils, hail and heatwaves that go to make up our ever-changing weather.

He wrote 'Frosts, Freezes and Fairs' chronicling all the great winters of the past when the Thames, Medway and Ouse froze and magnificent fairs and carnivals were held on the ice. He gave a series of lectures at Somerset House in London about the frost fairs and his book was instrumental in the making of a programme about the subject in December 2008 for BBC Radio 4, with Ian being one of the participants. As a speaker, Ian has given several thousand talks to a variety of clubs and societies.

Being a former teacher, Ian has been to scores of schools and enthused children of all ages and he is author of 'I Spy Weather'. He wrote a series of articles on the subject of 'Storms' for the National Curriculum for Primary education and gave a series of weather lectures to children and their parents during August 2010 at the Royal Institute in London. He helped set up a permanent display about weather sayings at the new Museum of the Southwest in Falmouth and has provided weather displays for the Greenwich Maritime

Museum and contributed to an exhibition about frost fairs at London's Guildhall. Ian is secretary to the Climatological Observers Link running several fully-equipped weather stations and is a Fellow of the Royal Meteorological Society.

His enthusiasm for the subject has led to a number of television appearances over the years. Ian presented the weather on BBC South Inside Out Series, The One Show on BBC TV talking about frost fairs and the BBC 1 Weather Show describing Gilbert White's eighteenth century weather observations at Selborne in Hampshire. He appeared on Channel 4's Big Breakfast Show and took part on Carlton Television's programme made to highlight the 10th anniversary of the October 1987 Storm. Ian has appeared on Channel 5's Weather Watch, on Meridian TV in the Rural Rides Series and BBC TV's Country File. He took part in BBC 1's Wild Weather in September 2010 in both the London and South regions, the latter analysing his long-range forecasts with excellent results. On radio Ian was heard talking about London fogs on BBC Radio 4's Strange Weather Day series and was a guest on Radio 4's Mid Week interviewed by Libby Purvis. He is the weatherman on the BBC Surrey and Sussex gardening programme 'Dig it'.

Ian has also brought back memories of The Beatles and bubble cars as co-author of the popular 'Surrey in the Sixties' and the sequel 'Surrey in the Seventies'. Every week he writes a weather column in local newspapers including the Surrey Mirror and Croydon Advertiser and the national Garden News. He has been weather consultant to insurance companies and firms and provides regular forecasts for a well-known vineyard, Ridgeview in Sussex and to agricultural contractors and farms. He is married with two sons and lives in Surrey.

## Short Bibliography

**Richard Inwards** amassed a large collection of proverbs, sayings and rules concerning the weather in his book Weather Lore first published in 1893 by Elliot Stock, London. There have been various editions but one more recently was produced in 1994 by Senate, an imprint of Studio Editions Ltd. ISBN 1 85958 054 8

**Paul J Marriott**, a professional meteorologist has put to the test many hundreds of sayings in his book Red Sky at Night, Shepherd's Delight. Published by Sheba Books. ISBN 0 9505730 5 1

**Paul John Goldsack** has written a practical book on weather lore called Weatherwise. It is devised for sailors and outdoor people. Published by David and Charles. ISBN 0-7153-8788-X

**Ian Currie** devised Red Sky at Night–Weather Sayings for all Seasons. Though currently out of print it looks at weather sayings on a monthly basis explaining what they mean and whether they can be relied on. Published by Frosted Earth. ISBN 978-0-9516710-2-3

# Books written or co-written by Ian Currie
# Available from Frosted Earth.

| | | |
|---|---|---|
| Red Sky at Night–Weather Sayings for All Seasons | ISBN 0-9516710-2-2 | out of print |
| Frost, Freezes and Fairs | ISBN 0-9516710-8-1 | £8.95 |
| I Spy Weather | ISBN 1-856571-131-5 | out of print |
| The Surrey Weather Book | ISBN 0-9516710-6-5 | £12.95 |
| The Dorset Weather Book | ISBN 0-9531603-0-0 | out of print |
| The Hampshire and Isle of Wight Weather Book | ISBN 1-872337-20-1 | £9.95 |
| The Berkshire Weather Book | ISBN 1-872337-48-1 | £9.95 |
| The Norfolk and Suffolk Weather Book | ISBN 1-872337-99-6 | out of print |
| The Sussex Weather Book | ISBN 1-872337-13-9 | out of print |
| The Kent Weather Book | ISBN 1-872337-85-6 | £12.99 |
| The Essex Weather Book | ISBN 1-872337-31-7 | £10.99 |
| Surrey in the Hurricane | ISBN 0-9513019-2-6 | £7.95 |
| London's Hurricane | ISBN 0-9513019-3-4 | £7.95 |
| Surrey in the Sixties | ISBN 0-9516710-4-9 | £12.95 |
| Surrey in the Seventies | ISBN 0-9516710-7-3 | £12.95 |

Ian Currie also edits Weather eye, a magazine for all interested in the weather.
Currently Weather eye is £2.95 per copy
3 issues plus post  £9.50
6 issues plus post  £17.50

Cumulonimbus over London looking north from Coulsdon 20.20hrs 16th August 1997.

ISBN 978-0-9531603-1-0

Price:
£5.95

9 780953 160310 >